OWN WHO YOU ARE

BRAIN TRAINING WORKBOOK FOR PERFORMERS

Amanda Ferranti, CMPC, Sean McMannis,
Samara Carranza and Raeanna McMannis

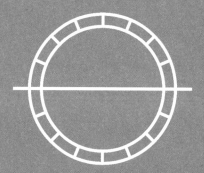

Own Who You Are
A Foundations Workbook For All Performance Individuals and Team – Ages 12 and Up

Edition 1 – Brain Training
Copyright © 2020 Amanda Ferranti, Sean McMannis
Published by Compete Well Media
5 A's Emotional Management Process Copyright © 2019 Amanda Ferranti
ALL RIGHTS RESERVED
Photography Jimmy Chung (Jimmychung.com)
Graphic Designer - Alex Steele (Asteelecreative.com) and Vicky Bumgarner
Editor – Kylie Kenyon
Co Authors – Samara Carranza and Raeanna McMannis

Printed in Canada

OWN WHO YOU ARE

BRAIN TRAINING WORKBOOK FOR PERFORMERS

FOUNDATION OWN WHO YOU ARE
CONTENTS

COMPETE
well

ABOUT
COMPETE WELL

Compete Well is committed to harnessing the methods of sport psychology by offering a creative, practical, and user-friendly platform to supplement competitors and leaders in their journey for personal growth and achievement. We are a company who passionately believes in the power of self-assessment and emotional management and are driven to continually learn and improve as professionals.

The Foundations workbook is the first of a series, designed from years of experience consulting and coaching performers in various sports. This workbook is specifically focused on helping you to develop the fundamental routines to build and maintain confidence, joy, and pride. By the end of this training, it is our goal to provide you with practical tools that you can use in moments of emotional discomfort (e.g. after mistakes or in preparation for an important performance). The activities are strategic and systematically laid out to foster a growth mindset, strengthen self-esteem and ultimately enhance your performance outcomes.

WORKBOOK TRAINING KEY

Read through the entire key and get accustomed to the terms and processes used in the Foundations Workbook.

ACTIVITY LOG

Every Section will begin with an Activity Log for you to keep track of your progress. All you have to do is check the box next to each activity once completed. The purpose of this process is to help you stay organized, motivated, and focused with a growth mindset.

DAILY ACTION TRACKER

There are two powerful actions that you will learn in this workbook: 1) Visit your WELL and 2) Practice Belly Breathing. In order for these actions to be effective, you must develop them into routines. To help you with this process, we have developed the Daily Action Tracker. You will be asked to make a mark on each day of the week that you visit your WELL and/or practice belly breathing. And if you stay in a chapter for more than one week, continue to add marks and keep track of your progress.

LET'S TALK

Each activity in your workbook will begin with Let's Talk. The goal of this text is to give you a basic understanding of how the activity will impact your performance and why it is important to your success. Consider this to be a brief speech by your brain training coach. Once you have gained this knowledge, you will read the Let's Take Action bullet points and complete the tasks of the activity.

LET'S TAKE ACTION

☐ Read each action, perform the task, and check the box when completed.

SECTION GOALS

At the completion of each chapter you will be guided in setting goals or action plans for the upcoming week. For better commitment and success, be sure that these goals are S.M.A.R.T. (Specific, Measurable, Achievable, Realistic, and Time-Bound).

UNIT CHALLENGE

Below the Chapter Goals, you will see a Unit Challenge. This is an extra activity related to the chapter content that is designed to elevate your development.

EMOJI

When you see this emoji, please flip to My Emotion Chart and select the emotion(s) that you feel in connection with the activity.

TOOLBOX

When you see this symbol, please flip to My Toolbox and read through the list of actions. This list is designed to give you some ideas. Keep in mind that you are not limited to this list and you are free to add your own action plans.

EMOTIONAL MANAGEMENT FRAMEWORK

LET'S TALK Sport psychology is an interdisciplinary science that can help you gain control over your brain and body. Throughout this workbook, you will be given lessons from physiology, psychology, biology, and sociology, that are designed to promote performance consistency and excellence. To begin, take a look at the Emotional Management Framework developed by Amanda Ferranti, CMPC (2019). Study each of the 5 components and learn how they all connect. Then, as you progress through the workbook, you will build awareness of this relationship and apply it to your own experiences. In the process, we urge you to continually return to the Emotional Management Framework and review it for deeper comprehension.

LET'S TAKE ACTION

- [ ] Read each of the components.
- [ ] Read My Toolbox in the Reference section.
- [ ] Read My Emotion Chart in the Reference section.
- [ ] Think of a trigger and how it impacts your arousal, emotions, thoughts, and performance / behaviors.

TRIGGERS

Triggers can be anything in the environment or within your brain that sparks a change in your arousal, thoughts, and/or emotions. Triggers can be both positive or negative and they are unique to each individual. This training will ask you to identify the specific triggers that disrupt or distract you from performing. Examples are losing, making mistakes, getting yelled at OR even winning, doing well, and receiving praise. Once you become aware of your triggers, you can develop action plans to prevent them from impacting your performance.

AROUSAL, EMOTIONS, THOUGHTS

Once a trigger is experienced, your body will respond with changes in arousal (your physiological state), emotions, and thoughts. Such changes can range from negative to positive and can be felt at various intensities. For example, if I make a mistake, my body will experience the discomfort of disappointment and my thoughts will become negative. Now, if I make that same mistake again and again, that sensation of disappointment will get stronger and I will have even more negative thoughts. In this book you will be trained to connect with your arousal, emotions, and thoughts as the first step to gaining control and making a change.

BEHAVIOR / PERFORMANCE

Your performance and/or behavior will be impacted by any changes that get triggered in your body. For example, you may hesitate in your decision when triggered by oppositional pressure or you may blame others after you make a mistake. In this book, you will be challenged to recognize and change your behaviors if they are not helping you to perform at your best.

TRIGGERS
+ Success, winning, praise, joy, awards
— Mistakes, losing, criticism, coach, parents, teammates, refs, pressure

AROUSAL

EMOTIONS

THOUGHTS

PERFORMANCE / BEHAVIOR
+ Fluid movements, energized, supportive, communicative, motivated, focused
— Hesitate, blame, complain, yell, foul, avoid, cry, lazy

ESTABLISH YOURSELF

MY DREAM GOAL IS:

WHICH EMOTION(S) WOULD YOU FEEL IF YOUR DREAM GOAL WERE TO BECOME A REALITY? 😃

WHO WILL BE WITH YOU ON THIS JOURNEY?

- ☐
- ☐
- ☐
- ☐
- ☐

THE PEOPLE I CAN RELY ON FOR SUPPORT ON THIS JOURNEY WILL BE...

- ☐
- ☐
- ☐
- ☐
- ☐

IN THE NEAR FUTURE I WOULD LIKE TO IMPROVE...

- ☐
- ☐
- ☐
- ☐
- ☐

IN THE LONG-TERM I WOULD LIKE TO IMPROVE...

- ☐
- ☐
- ☐
- ☐
- ☐

MY FAVORITE PERFORMANCE MEMORY AS A KID IS...

MY HOBBIES / INTERESTS ARE:

☐

☐

☐

☐

☐

THE BEST THING ABOUT MY PERFORMANCE ACTIVITY:

☐ Spending time with teammates/peers

☐ Experiencing new opportunities

☐ Accomplishing a goal that I have set for myself

☐ Allowing failure to drive a new success

☐ Striving to complete a goal with others

I FEEL MOTIVATED WHEN...

☐ Someone verbally encourages me

☐ Someone challenges me

☐ I set a goal

☐ I try something new

☐ I'm incentivized by something

☐

I LOVE BEING AROUND PEOPLE WHO...

☐ Are being spontaneous and laid back

☐ Are ambitious and dedicated

☐ Challenge me to always get better

☐ Encourage me

☐ Share the same goals or values as me

☐

I AM OPEN TO START THE COMPETE WELL - OWN WHO YOU ARE JOURNEY BECAUSE...

MY WELL

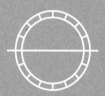

"DIG THE WELL BEFORE YOU
ARE THIRSTY."
- CHINESE PROVERB

MY WELL

INTRODUCTION

As a competitive and success-driven individual, what do you tend to focus on after a performance? I know for me, I often dwell on mistakes and get stuck feeling a mix of negative emotions. And I wouldn't be surprised if this happens for you too. You see, our brains are similar to technological devices in that we want to fix errors or "autocorrect." However, what's the difference between humans and a device? You got it – emotions! So when our attention is focused on the bad mistakes, we are left feeling frustrated, disappointed, or even angry and embarrassed. And if you don't accept and manage these feelings, they may get in the way of learning and developing.

To help you balance these natural "autocorrect" tendencies, you will be trained to use the WELL. Traditionally, a WELL stores the most important life-giving substance we rely on for health and vitality: water. The more water we have stored in the WELL, the more access we have to a powerful healing agent. As a performer, you will develop a personal WELL that stores memories of positive moments and progress. Like water, these memories can rejuvenate you to change your mindset, trust yourself, and boost your energy. And the more memories you add to your WELL, the greater access you have to feelings of pride, satisfaction, and confidence when needed.

At a glance, the WELL may seem like an easy task. You will simply keep a journal where you write and read about positive memories in your performance environment. However, we are asking you to establish a routine, and like any routine, this will require discipline and commitment to the process. To help you with this, use the Daily Action Tracker for motivation and trust that the WELL has been tested and proven to enhance confidence if used routinely.

MY WELL ACTIVITY LOG
Check the box when you complete the activity.

- ☐ **READ** // My Well Introduction
- ☐ **ACTIVITY 1.1** // My Performance Actions
- ☐ **ACTIVITY 1.2** // My Gratitude
- ☐ **ACTIVITY 1.3** // My Character
- ☐ **ACTIVITY 1.4** // My Wins, Rewards, and Praise

>> **MY WELL JOURNAL** // Use Routine

DAILY ACTION TRACKER
Make a mark on each day that you complete the activity.

Visited **MY WELL**

Practiced **BREATHING**

MY PERFORMANCE ACTIONS

LET'S TALK

In this section of your WELL, you will highlight any controllable actions that you are proud of - regardless of the outcome. For instance, let's say you score a point or do your personal best. What did you do to make it happen? HOW did you get this achievement? Also keep in mind that you can feel proud in moments that didn't go as planned. For example, you make a great pass, but your teammate doesn't receive it. Or maybe you've made a mistake, yet you feel proud about the way you responded. In either case, be sure to use detail when describing your actions. As a result, you will feel a greater sense of control over your progress and success.

LET'S TAKE ACTION

- [ ] Think of 2 proud moments and describe what you did to make them happen in the space below.
- [ ] Include the DATE and LOCATION of each moment.
- [ ] Identify which emotion(s) you feel while recording your memory.

1. *EXAMPLE:*

6/11/19 - In the game against Rage, I realized that my teammates weren't communicating and we were breaking down on defense so I started to communicate more directions and our performance improved.

 Proud, Determined

2.

3.

MY GRATITUDE

LET'S TALK

As you will learn in Section 5, there is a strong emotional power associated with gratitude. In order to access this power, you must first develop a practice, or routine. To help you with this, we have created a separate section of the WELL for you to identify moments of gratitude on a weekly basis. As you follow the instructions, there are two important points to consider: 1) Be sure to record specific moments that you are grateful for, rather than a list of things or people (see example), and 2) You can include moments that occurred outside of your performance environment. Remember, a strong gratitude practice will fill your brain with positive and calm emotions. And you will start to view challenges as opportunities, rather than threats.

LET'S TAKE ACTION

☐ Think of 2 moments or experiences that you are grateful for, or when you displayed gratitude toward someone, and describe what happened in the space below.

☐ Include the DATE and LOCATION of each moment.

☐ Identify which emotion(s) you feel while recording your memory.

1. *EXAMPLE:* 5/19/19 - I am grateful that coach organized a team trip to the adventure park on Long Island

 Excited, Happy

2.

3.

MY MOMENTS OF CHARACTER

LET'S TALK

In Section 4 you will learn that character is a choice in behavior. This means that you have full control over demonstrating traits, like competitiveness, determination, passion, intelligence, quickness, etc. For instance, maybe you showed leadership by communicating to your teammates OR you displayed hard work when you felt exhausted. Use this section of your WELL to celebrate who you are as a person and performer. When thinking of moments, keep in mind that your character is separate from outcomes or results. In fact, when you focus on your character traits it helps you to maintain your pride in times when you believe "I did nothing well."

LET'S TAKE ACTION!

- [ ] Think of 2 moments when your character was revealed, and describe what you did in the space below.
- [ ] Include the DATE and LOCATION of each moment.
- [ ] Identify which emotion(s) you feel while recording your memory.

1. EXAMPLE: 7/1/19 - At practice, I demonstrated perseverance and hard work when I got very tired, but kept pushing myself to stay focused and work hard.

 Proud, Satisfied

2.

3.

MY WINS, REWARDS, AND PRAISE

LET'S TALK Just think, do you have a tendency to forget all of your successes after a bad mistake, or when preparing for a stressful event? I know I do! In this section, you will keep track of observable outcomes like wins, rewards, and praise, or even breaking records and making a team. These moments are important to remember because they are associated with the strongest positive emotions, such as pride, satisfaction, and confidence. Also, by writing them down over time, you are compiling evidence that you are capable of progress and success. As a result, this section of your WELL can be called upon as a quick and effective tool to boost your energy and confidence at any time before, during, or after performances.

LET'S TAKE ACTION!

- [ ] Think of 2 moments when you won or received a reward or praise, and describe what happened in the space below.
- [ ] Include the DATE and LOCATION of each moment.
- [ ] Identify which emotion(s) you feel while recording your memory.

1. *EXAMPLE:* 6/30/19 - At Surf Cup Tournament: My teammates and coach told me that I did a great job and our team won!

 Happy, Proud

2.

3.

MY WELL
JOURNAL

FILL MY WELL

LET'S TALK

In Activities 1.1 through 1.4 you practiced making entries into each of the four sections of your WELL. Now it's time to develop a weekly routine that consists of two main actions: 1) Make 2-3 entries into your WELL after performances and then 2) Read through your entire WELL before performances. When you are writing entries on a weekly basis, you can choose which sections of the WELL to add to; however, be sure that you are gradually developing ALL four sections.

To help you feel motivated and disciplined with this process, remember that the WELL has been tested and proven to help performers in three distinct ways; 1) It shows evidence of progress and success, 2) It helps you build trust and confidence in yourself, and 3) It is an effective tool for generating positive emotions. Once your routine is well-established, you will find that it is easier to recall positive memories when you are triggered into an emotionally uncomfortable state (e.g. after a mistake, a loss, or getting yelled at).

MY ROUTINE

✓ Make 2-3 entries into your WELL after practices and competitions.

✓ Read your entire WELL prior to practices and competitions.

✓ Mark each day that you visit your WELL on your Daily Action Tracker.

✓ Recall your WELL when triggered into an emotionally uncomfortable state.

MY WELL JOURNAL

DATE & LOCATION AND WHAT HAPPENED

DATE & LOCATION AND WHAT HAPPENED

WHAT ARE YOU GRATEFUL FOR?
DATE & LOCATION AND WHAT HAPPENED

DATE & LOCATION AND WHAT HAPPENED
WINS, REWARDS, AND PRAISE

MY WELL JOURNAL

WHAT ARE YOU GRATEFUL FOR?
DATE & LOCATION AND WHAT HAPPENED

DATE & LOCATION AND WHAT HAPPENED
WINS, REWARDS, AND PRAISE

WHAT ARE YOU GRATEFUL FOR?
DATE & LOCATION AND WHAT HAPPENED

DATE & LOCATION AND WHAT HAPPENED

WINS, REWARDS, AND PRAISE

WHAT ARE YOU GRATEFUL FOR?

DATE & LOCATION AND WHAT HAPPENED

DATE & LOCATION AND WHAT HAPPENED

WINS, REWARDS, AND PRAISE

MY WELL JOURNAL

WHAT ARE YOU GRATEFUL FOR?
DATE & LOCATION AND WHAT HAPPENED

DATE & LOCATION AND WHAT HAPPENED

WINS, REWARDS, AND PRAISE

MY BREATHING

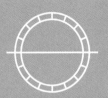

"THE ONLY WAY FORWARD IS TO TAKE
IT BREATH BY BREATH."
- MORGAN HARPER NICHOLS

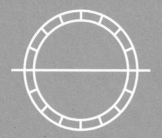

MY BREATHING

INTRODUCTION

As a performer, I think of my breathing as an essential tool to fuel my body for success. Many of us already know the power and necessity of breathing, but may not understand the science of when, how, or why our breathing changes — and we may not have the skills to regain control once a change has been triggered. To help you develop, this section of your training will challenge you to become aware of your breath and body and learn how to control your breathing for optimal performance.

Before beginning, I want you to first refer back to the Emotional Management Framework. Notice how your Arousal connects with Emotions and Thoughts, and how Triggers can start a chain reaction that impacts your Performance and Behaviors. Once a response is triggered in your body, you cannot control the changes that have been biologically signaled. Sometimes this response can help you perform, and sometimes it gets in your way and becomes a distraction.

For example, let's say you make a silly mistake and immediately your heart rate is elevated, your breathing is difficult, and your thoughts become rapid. This quick-acting arousal response has now changed your body to feel frustrated with tense muscles and an inability to focus. You will be happy to know that by completing this section of your training, you will be equipped with the quickest, easiest, and most effective tool to help you manage this response — breathing. In fact, with routine training and proper technique, breathing can help your body refocus, relax, and re-energize. You will also determine exactly when and how to use your breathing skills so that you are prepared for potential triggers in the future.

MY BREATHING ACTIVITY LOG
Check the box when you complete the activity.

☐ **READ** // My Breathing Introduction

☐ **ACTIVITY 2.1** // My Body Systems

☐ **ACTIVITY 2.2** // Access My Breath

☐ **ACTIVITY 2.3** // Target My Breath

☐ **ACTIVITY 2.4** // My Calming Response

☐ **ACTIVITY 2.5** // My Pre-Performance Routine

☐ **ACTIVITY 2.6** // My Performance Plan

☐ **ACTIVITY 2.7** // My Breathing Goals

DAILY ACTION TRACKER
Make a mark on each day that you complete the activity.

Visited **MY WELL**

Practiced **BREATHING**

MY BODY SYSTEMS

LET'S TALK

Our brain and all the systems it controls is designed with one major focus: to keep us safe. As a performer, there are two types of threat to your safety: one that is physical and another that is psychological. For example, your body will perceive a physical threat when a ball is flying toward your head whereas it will sense a psychological threat when you are losing or getting yelled at. In both cases, the body's sympathetic nervous system is activated, which is also known as the fight, flight, or freeze stress response. This reaction is precisely what gets your body to move toward safety. Conversely, when your brain interprets situations as safe, it activates your parasympathetic nervous system, which is designed to keep your body stable and thriving.

When competing at a high level, there is a certain degree of stress that is necessary in order to be alert, react quickly, and perform at your best; however, we cannot stay in this state of alarm for long because it exhausts our system quickly. With that said, study the diagrams in this activity and learn to identify the changes that are happening within your body. In doing so, you will gain greater control over balancing your sympathetic and parasympathetic nervous systems for optimal performance.

SYMPATHETIC NERVOUS SYSTEM
What happens when my body is
STRESSED?

THOUGHTS
Rapid
Difficult to focus

EYES
Vision is narrowed

LUNGS
Breathing is shallow
Oxygen decreases

HEART
Pumps faster

GUT
Inactive
Digestion slows

MUSCLES
Tension goes up
Quick actions

MY BODY SYSTEMS

PARASYMPATHETIC NERVOUS SYSTEM

What happens when my body is CALM?

THOUGHTS
Slower
Can learn & plan

EYES
Vision is broader

LUNGS
Breathing deep
Oxygen increases

HEART
Pumps steady

GUT
Active digestion

MUSCLES
Tension goes down
More relaxed

LET'S TAKE ACTION !

☐ Study the diagram to be more aware of how the changes in your body systems impact your performance.

☐ Answer the questions to help you build awareness and control.

Reflect on your performances and make a list of triggers that signal your sympathetic nervous system and cause you to feel stressed.

Which of these body functions can you control to help yourself calm down?

HINT: What is this section called?

In addition to breathing, what could you do to activate the parasympathetic nervous system and help yourself calm down?

ACCESS MY BREATH

You may laugh at the idea that we are teaching you how to breathe, but did you know that the diaphragm is a muscle that works to expand your lungs? And like all other muscles in your body, you can strengthen the diaphragm through repetition. The specific repetition that you must practice at home is called deep breathing, or belly breathing exercises. As a result of this training, your diaphragm will be more prepared to expand your lungs and access your breath under stress. Without this training, it will be much harder to calm down and stay focused on performing. Once this exercise is completed, continue to use your Daily Action Tracker and make breathing a part of your daily routine.

LET'S
TAKE
ACTION

☐ Practice Deep Breathing by following the steps below.

Fold down this corner to come back and reference the belly breathing routine!

BELLY BREATHING ROUTINE

Before beginning: Sit up straight in a comfortable position. Relax your shoulders away from your ears. Place one hand on your heart, the other hand on your belly.

1. Take a full, deep inhalation through your nose.

2. Feel your belly push your hand out. The hand on your chest should remain still.

3. Purse your lips as if you were going to whistle.

4. Exhale slowly through your mouth. Feel your belly draw back toward your spine.

5. Close your eyes. Repeat 5 more times.

Exhale slowly through your mouth

Inhale through your nose

Feel your belly draw back to your spine

Feel your belly push against your hand

MY BREATH ACTIVITY 2.2

TARGET MY BREATH

LET'S TALK

Now that you can recognize broad changes in your body systems and you know how to use breathing to calm down, it is time to locate where each emotion is felt within your body. For example, I feel anxiety as a tension in my head, tightening in my chest, and shakiness in my hands. Whereas I feel anger as a heaviness in my shoulders and a clenching in my jaw. By recognizing these subtle differences, you will be more aware and prepared to manage yourself. Remember e-motions are energy in motion throughout your body. If this energy is disruptive or distracting, pay attention to the areas of your body that are affected. Then, you can use your breathing skills and focus the movement of your exhalation breath toward the designated areas within your body. For instance, when I recognize that my body is feeling anxious, I can visualize my breath traveling to my head, chest, and hands. This will help create space in your body and move the negative energy out of your systems.

LET'S TAKE ACTION

- [ ] Locate where you feel each emotion in your body and use the designated color to shade the area(s) in the figure. (several colors may overlap)
- [ ] When you feel each emotion, target your breath toward the designated area(s) of your body.

TARGET MY BREATH

ANGER / FRUSTRATION

EXCITED / HAPPY

DISAPPOINTMENT / SADNESS

RELIEVED / OPTIMISTIC

ANXIETY/FEAR

PEACEFUL/CALM

EMBARRASSMENT

CONFIDENT / DETERMINED

MY CALMING RESPONSE

LET'S TALK

Depending upon your performance environment, there is often not enough time to stop and use the belly breathing techniques. To overcome this problem, you can train your body to activate a calming response by using a quick cue word or image. For example, if your coach is yelling at you in the middle of your performance, you can remind yourself, "It's okay," or imagine a peaceful sunset. In order for this cue word or image to be effective, you must focus on it while practicing your belly breathing at home. This will create an association that activates a calming response. Be creative and personal in your words and images to ensure that they are effective. Also, this activity will prepare you with a mantra to refocus and shift your attention back to performing.

LET'S TAKE ACTION!

- [ ] Choose a cue word.
- [ ] Decide on a calming image.
- [ ] Complete the mantra.

CUE WORD:

While you are practicing breathing, determine a cue word or brief phrase to be associated with a calming response. As you can see in the examples, keep it short and written as if you are talking to yourself. What do you want to hear?

EXAMPLE:

STEADY

BREATHE

CALM

RELAX

CENTER

FOCUS

BALANCE

PAUSE

IT'S OKAY

WHAT IS YOUR CUE WORD?

MY CALMING RESPONSE

CALMING IMAGE:

While you are practicing breathing, create a vivid image to be associated with a calming response. This image could be anything that is calming, such as your favorite place to visit, the flow of water, or even your beloved pet.

MANTRA:

Practice the following mantra to help you refocus and shift your attention back to performing. For example, you can say I am ready to "compete," "be a leader," or "take risks." When determining how to complete the mantra, consider what will get you motivated.

MY BODY IS **ALERT**,

MY MIND IS **FOCUSED**.

I AM READY TO

MY PRE-PERFORMANCE ROUTINE

LET'S TALK

For those of you who are not familiar with a pre-performance routine, it is simply a sequence of thoughts and actions that a performer will systematically use prior to a competition. In other words, it's a way to "get in the zone." In this activity, you will either write down your current routine or create one using some ideas in the key below. Then, you will consider the emotions that you feel at each moment prior to your performance and determine if breathing will help you prepare. For example, if you feel nervous, anxious, or even overly-excited, you can integrate breathing techniques to help yourself calm down and stay focused. By planning ahead, you are giving your body the best chance of performing to its potential.

LET'S TAKE ACTION

☐ Write down your pre-performance routine in the numbered boxes.
☐ Circle the lungs icon in each step of your routine where you will include breathing techniques.
☐ Identify which breathing technique you will use from Activities 2.2, 2.3, and 2.4.
☐ Next time you have a performance, include breathing in your routine.

KEY: Choose from the following routine ideas or create your own...

Drive to performance

Get equipment ready

Put on your equipment a special way

Listen to music, warm up

Other _____

Pre-performance meal / snack

Ritual before performance starts

Pre-performance shower

Stretch

MY PRE-PERFORMANCE ROUTINE

1. *MY ROUTINE:*

2. *MY ROUTINE:*

3. *MY ROUTINE:*

4. *MY ROUTINE:*

5. *MY ROUTINE:*

FINISH:
THE PERFORMANCE

MY PERFORMANCE PLAN

LET'S TALK

As you've learned from Activity 2.1, triggers can activate a biological response that hurts your performance — and breathing is the most powerful tool to help yourself calm down and refocus. In this activity you will identify three different triggers that disrupt or distract you from performing well. Then, for each of the triggers you will determine which of your newly learned breathing techniques will help you the most. This activity is just another level of preparation to help you overcome difficult situations and perform consistently at your best.

LET'S TAKE ACTION

- ☐ Identify the triggers that make you physically uncomfortable.
- ☐ Label the emotion(s) you feel and shade the areas of your body that are affected.
- ☐ Develop a plan to help yourself stay focused when these triggers arise.

TRIGGER:

☺ EMOTION:

Shade the area(s) of your body that are affected:

Circle your plan:

Breathe:

Calming Image:

Cue Word:

Mantra:
My mind is alert,
my body is focused,
I am ready to:

----------------   ----------------

MY PERFORMANCE CHALLENGE

TRIGGER:

 EMOTION:

Shade the area(s) of your body that are affected:

Circle your plan:

Breathe:

Cue Word:

Calming Image:

Mantra:
My mind is alert,
my body is focused,
I am ready to:

TRIGGER:

 EMOTION:

Shade the area(s) of your body that are affected:

Circle your plan:

Breathe:

Cue Word:

Calming Image:

Mantra:
My mind is alert,
my body is focused,
I am ready to:

MY BREATHING GOALS

I want to strengthen my diaphragm, so I will ....

....

....

I want to enter my performance focused and alert, so I will ....

....

....

I want to refocus after my body is triggered, so I will ....

....

....

UNIT CHALLENGE

Are YOU up for the challenge?!

Practice deep breathing every day for at least 2-3 minutes. As you breathe, challenge your thoughts to focus on a cue word, a calming image, or the mantra you worked on in Activity 2.4.

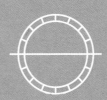

I WANT,
I WILL,
I CAN,
I AM.

MY CORE VALUES

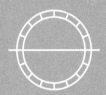

"IT'S NOT HARD TO MAKE
DECISIONS WHEN YOU KNOW WHAT
YOUR VALUES ARE."
- ROY DISNEY

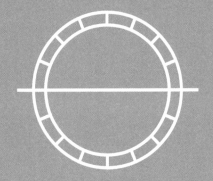

MY CORE VALUES

INTRODUCTION

Whether you realize it or not, all of your decisions and behaviors in life are driven by a set of core values. To better understand what is meant by core values, we will define them as your strong beliefs and philosophies held about life and your own purpose. For example, I may choose to train every day because I value commitment and success. Or I may decide to stay calm when provoked because I value compassion and respect. In both examples, my core values are strong beliefs about what I want in my life (my goals) and how I pursue those goals (my decisions and behaviors).

In this section you will identify and connect with your core values. Doing so will activate several performance benefits, including greater control over decisions and behaviors. And when you feel more in control of your decisions and behaviors, you are likely to feel more positive emotions like confidence, pride, and security.

Additionally, you will learn to identify moments or triggers when your core values are challenged. Keep in mind that your values are a choice, which means you will encounter others who may not share, understand, or accept your value-driven behaviors. For example, someone may ask you to lie about something and if you value honesty, you are faced with a choice that can feel emotionally uncomfortable. Or if you value humility, it may annoy you to hear someone gloat about their success. If a situation challenges your core values or if someone chooses values that are different from yours, it's okay. In this section you will learn how to recognize these triggers, both within yourself and with others, and develop goals or action plans to strengthen your value-driven behaviors.

CORE VALUES ACTIVITY LOG
Check the box when you complete the activity.

☐ **READ //** My Core Values Introduction

☐ **ACTIVITY 3.1 //** My Core Values List

☐ **ACTIVITY 3.2 //** My Top 3 Core Values

☐ **ACTIVITY 3.3 //** Uphold My Core Values

☐ **ACTIVITY 3.4 //** Strengthen My Core Values

☐ **ACTIVITY 3.5 //** My Core Values Goals

DAILY ACTION TRACKER
Make a mark on each day that you complete the activity.

Visited **MY WELL**

Practiced **BREATHING**

MY CORE VALUES LIST

LET'S TALK As you can see from the list below, there are a variety of values - some that you will relate with and others you may not. Use this activity to develop a stronger awareness of which values are most important to YOU. In doing so, you will gain another tool to help establish your goals, make secure decisions, and navigate emotional discomfort.

LET'S TAKE ACTION!
- [ ] Read through the entire list of core values below.
- [ ] Circle 10 core values that you connect with the most.

ACCEPTANCE
To be accepted as I am

ACHIEVEMENT
To have important accomplishments

ADVENTURE
To have new and exciting experiences

AUTHORITY
To be in charge of and responsible for others

AUTONOMY
To be self-determined and independent

BEAUTY
To appreciate beauty around me

CARING
To take care of others

CHALLENGE
To take on difficult tasks and problems

COMMITMENT
To make enduring, meaningful commitments

COMPASSION
To feel and act on concern for others

CONTRIBUTION
To make a lasting contribution in the world

COOPERATION
To work collaboratively with others

COURTESY
To be considerate and polite towards others

CREATIVITY
To have new and original ideas

DEPENDABILITY
To be reliable and trustworthy

DUTY
To carry out my duties and obligations

EXCITEMENT
To have a life full of thrills and stimulation

FAITHFULNESS
To be loyal and true relationships

FAME
To be known and recognized

FAMILY
To have a happy, loving family

MY CORE VALUES LIST

FITNESS
To be physically fit and strong

FLEXIBILITY
To adjust to new circumstances easily

FORGIVENESS
To be forgiving of others

FRIENDSHIP
To have close, supportive friends

FUN
To play and have fun

GENEROSITY
To give what I have to others

GENUINENESS
To act in a manner that is true to who I am

GOD'S WILL
To seek and obey the will of God

GROWTH
To keep changing and growing

HEALTH
To be physically well and healthy

HELPFULNESS
To be helpful to others

HONESTY
To be honest and truthful

HOPE
To maintain a positive and optimistic outlook

HUMILITY
To be modest and unassuming

HUMOR
To see the humorous side of myself and the world

INDEPENDENCE
To be free from dependence on others

INNER PEACE
To experience personal peace

JUSTICE
To promote fair and equal treatment for all

KNOWLEDGE
To learn and contribute valuable knowledge

LOVING
To give love to others

MASTERY
To be competent in my everyday activity

MINDFULNESS
To live conscious and mindful of the present moment

OPENNESS
To be open to new experiences, ideas and options

ORDER
To have life that is well ordered and organized

PASSION
To have deep feelings about ideas, activities, or people

PLEASURE
To feel good

POPULARITY
To be well liked by many people

POWER
To have control over others

PURPOSE
To have meaning and direction in my life

RESPONSIBILITY
To make and carry out responsible decisions

RISK
To take risks and chances

SAFETY
To be safe and secure

SELF-ACCEPTANCE
To accept myself as I am

SELF-CONTROL
To be disciplined in my own actions

SELF-ESTEEM
To feel good about myself

SERVICE
To be of service to others

SPIRITUALITY
To grow and mature spiritually

STABILITY
To have a life that stays fairly consistent

TOLERANCE
To accept and respect those who differ from me

TRADITION
To follow respected patterns of the past

VIRTUE
To live a morally pure and excellent life

WEALTH
To have plenty of money

OTHER VALUE:

.

.

.

MY TOP 3 CORE VALUES

LET'S TALK Now that you have a broad picture of which values are most important in your life, it's time to select the top three that you believe in the most. This may seem like a difficult task; however, this narrowing process will help you develop a deeper connection to your core values with the strongest influence. Your top three core values can then be used as a compass – a quick and reliable tool to help you navigate your journey.

LET'S TAKE ACTION
- Review your top 10 core values from Activity 3.1.
- Select your top 3 core values and write them in the space below.
- Briefly describe why each of the core values is important to you.
- Write about a time when you demonstrated each core value.
- Describe a time when each value affected a decision you made.

CORE VALUE 1: _____

1. _____ is important to me because _____

_____

_____

2. I demonstrated _____ when _____

_____

_____

3. A time when the value _____ affected a decision I made

was _____

_____

MY TOP 3 CORE VALUES

CORE VALUE 2: _____

1. _____ is important to me because _____

_____

_____

2. I demonstrated _____ when _____

_____

_____

3. A time when the value _____ affected a decision I made was _____

_____

CORE VALUE 3: _____

1. _____ is important to me because _____

_____

_____

2. I demonstrated _____ when _____

_____

_____

3. A time when the value _____ affected a decision I made was _____

_____

UPHOLD MY CORE VALUES

LET'S TALK

Although you have identified and connected with your core values, it is not always easy to maintain them. In fact, there will be many times when you are internally challenged and do not uphold your values. As a result, you may feel disappointed in yourself, which could negatively impact your performance. By building awareness of triggers, you can prepare yourself to choose your positive core values during difficult situations. You will then find that the more your decisions are in-line with your core values, the more at ease you will be with yourself, and the better you will perform.

LET'S TAKE ACTION

☐ Write out your top 3 core values from Activity 3.2.
☐ Describe a moment when you were disappointed in your behavior because it conflicted with your values.
☐ Identify what triggered you to behave in this way.
☐ Determine what you can do to maintain your core value.

CORE VALUE 1: _____

I was disappointed when I...

_____

_____

I was triggered to behave this way because...

_____

_____

Next time I am faced with this trigger, I will

_____

_____

UPHOLD MY CORE VALUES

CORE VALUE 2: _____

I was disappointed when I...

I was triggered to behave this way because...

Next time I am faced with this trigger, I will

CORE VALUE 3: _____

I was disappointed when I...

I was triggered to behave this way because...

Next time I am faced with this trigger, I will

STRENGTHEN MY CORE VALUES

LET'S TALK As you've learned, values are a choice and unique to each individual. That means that you will most likely confront - or be confronted by - others who do not share or demonstrate your core values. This will result in conflict, or emotional discomfort. Just think, is there someone in your performance environment that you continually experience conflict with? This activity will help you to identify the values guiding the other person's behaviors. In doing so, you will learn to empathize, or see their point of view, and better understand the root of the conflict. As a result, you can prepare for future interactions and stay focused on strengthening the core values that are most important to you.

LET'S TAKE ACTION!

- [ ] Describe a moment of emotional discomfort (conflict) and identify how you felt.
- [ ] Identify which core value was being challenged.
- [ ] Consider the values that were driving the behaviors of the other person(s) involved.
- [ ] Determine what you can do when faced with the conflict in the future.

1. 😃 I felt _____ when _____

_____

_____

Which of your core values were being challenged?		Which values do you think were guiding the other person involved?
_____	**VS.**	_____
_____		_____
_____		_____

 What can you do when faced with this conflict of values in the future?

_____

_____

STRENGTHEN MY CORE VALUES

2. 😄 I felt _____ when _____

_____

_____

Which of your core values were being challenged?		Which values do you think were guiding the other person involved?
_____	**VS.**	_____
_____		_____
_____		_____

What can you do when faced with this conflict of values in the future?

_____

_____

_____

3. 😄 I felt _____ when _____

_____

_____

Which of your core values were being challenged?		Which values do you think were guiding the other person involved?
_____	**VS.**	_____
_____		_____
_____		_____

What can you do when faced with this conflict of values in the future?

_____

_____

CORE VALUES WEEKLY GOALS

I want to strengthen my value of _growth_ , so
I will _manage my frustrations by breathing instead of blaming others_

and focus on what I can do to make small improvements.

I want to strengthen my value of , so
I will

I want to strengthen my value of , so
I will

I want to resolve conflict so I will _be more aware of how my values may_

differ from others and remember that I cannot control other people.

I want to resolve conflict so I will

I want to resolve conflict so I will

UNIT CHALLENGE

Are YOU up for the challenge?!

After reviewing your core values and setting a goal, ask a family member, a friend, or someone close if they agree with your core values, or whether they see things differently. Be open, be vulnerable, and be challenged.

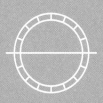

I WANT,
I WILL,
I CAN,
I AM.

MY CHARACTER

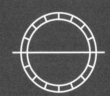

"IT IS OUR CHOICES THAT SHOW
WHAT WE TRULY ARE, FAR MORE
THAN OUR ABILITIES."
- JK ROWLING

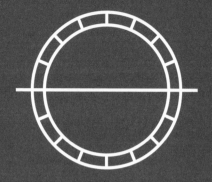

MY CHARACTER

INTRODUCTION

There are many who believe that sports build character. But the truth is — they actually reveal it. And this is important because character doesn't just happen. It's a choice in behavior that you must work to uphold and strengthen. To help you understand what we mean by character we will define it as a set of traits or descriptive words used to represent consistent patterns of behavior, thoughts, and emotions over time. For example, I believe that I am committed, smart, and passionate because I have showed these behaviors throughout my athletic and professional career.

So does that mean I demonstrate these traits ALL the time? Not at all. Your traits are not black-or-white. Meaning, you can still be considered smart without demonstrating smarts ALL the time. In fact, it's often the moments when we fall short of our character that are most uncomfortable. For example, you may feel embarrassed and frustrated if you are losing because you highly identify with being competitive. Or maybe you feel disappointed because you messed up your skills, yet you consider yourself to be technical. In this section, you will be trained to overcome these moments of emotional discomfort by developing a stronger understanding and connection with your character. As a result, you will have a reliable tool for a boost of energy or positive feelings when needed.

While you are working through this section, keep in mind that many young performers struggle to identify their own character traits for two main reasons. For some, it may feel arrogant or conceited to highlight your positive qualities. If this is the case, keep in mind that there is a difference between boasting to others and connecting with who you are. For others, you may be hesitant to commit to your traits because of doubt or fear. In either case, use this section to be open, honest, and self-reflective. As a result, you will replace doubt with pride, and fear with confidence. You will learn to OWN WHO YOU ARE!

MY CHARACTER ACTIVITY LOG

Check the box when you complete the activity.

- ☐ **READ //** My Character Introduction
- ☐ **ACTIVITY 4.1 //** My Character Trait List
- ☐ **ACTIVITY 4.2 //** My Top 3 Character Traits
- ☐ **ACTIVITY 4.3 //** Remember My Character Traits
- ☐ **ACTIVITY 4.4 //** Strengthen My Character Traits
- ☐ **ACTIVITY 4.5 //** My Character Goals

DAILY ACTION TRACKER

Make a mark on each day that you complete the activity.

Visited **MY WELL**

Practiced **BREATHING**

MY CHARACTER TRAIT LIST

LET'S TALK

Take a moment to reflect - which words can you use to describe yourself both as a performer and a person? How would your team-mates, coach, or parents describe you? You may be hesitant to select a trait but remember that they are patterns or tendencies, which means that you may not ALWAYS demonstrate that behavior perfectly. Just think of the example, if I am determined, am I determined ALL the time? Absolutely not! Use this exercise to freely describe yourself and create a snapshot of your unique collection of character traits.

LET'S TAKE ACTION

☐ Read through the entire list of character traits below.

☐ Identify and circle the character traits that best describe you.

ACCEPTING	DETERMINED
ATHLETIC	DOWN TO EARTH
AWARE	DRIVEN
BALANCED	ENTHUSIASTIC
BRAVE	FLEXIBLE
CHEERFUL	FOCUSED
COMMITTED	FORGIVING
COMPETITIVE	FRIENDLY
CONFIDENT	GENEROUS
COOPERATIVE	GOOFY
COURTEOUS	GRATEFUL
CREATIVE	HARDWORKING
DECISIVE	HELPFUL

MY CHARACTER TRAIT LIST

HONEST	POSITIVE
HUMBLE	PRACTICAL
INDEPENDENT	REALISTIC
INNOVATIVE	RELAXED
INSIGHTFUL	RELIABLE
INTELLIGENT	RESILIENT
INTUITIVE	RESPECTFUL
KIND	RESPONSIBLE
LISTENER	SELF-DIRECTED
LOYAL	SELFLESS
MATURE	SENSITIVE
MODEST	SERIOUS
MOTIVATED	SKILLED
NURTURING	SMART
OPEN MINDED	STRONG
OPTIMISTIC	THOUGHTFUL
ORGANIZED	TOLERANT
PASSIONATE	TOUGH
PATIENT	TRUSTING
PERCEPTIVE	
PERSISTENT	

MY TOP 3 CHARACTER TRAITS

LET'S TALK Now that you have a broad picture of your character, it's time to select the top three traits that you feel the strongest connection with — the ones that make you feel the most proud and confident as a performer. You will then determine how often you demonstrate each trait. This will prove that your character can be secure without being perfect. For instance, even the hardest worker will take breaks at times. The key objective of this activity is to develop a deeper connection with yourself. As a result, you will establish a strong foundation to face emotional triggers in the future.

LET'S TAKE ACTION !

- [ ] Review your character trait list from Activity 4.1.
- [ ] Select the top 3 character traits that you identify with the most.
- [ ] Rate the % of time that you demonstrate each trait.
- [ ] Write about specific actions you do that demonstrate each trait.
- [ ] Identify which emotion(s) you feel while recording your actions.

I AM _____ E ⌒ F SHADE IN AMOUNT _____ **%** OF THE TIME

I know I am _____ because _____

_____

_____

☺ Which emotion(s) do you feel when you reflect _____

_____

_____

MY TOP 3 CHARACTER TRAITS

I AM

SHADE IN
AMOUNT

%
OF
THE
TIME

I know I am _____ because _____

_____

😃 Which emotion(s) do you feel when you reflect _____

_____

I AM

SHADE IN
AMOUNT

%
OF
THE
TIME

I know I am _____ because _____

_____

😃 Which emotion(s) do you feel when you reflect _____

_____

REMEMBER MY CHARACTER TRAITS

LET'S TALK

As you've experienced in Activity 4.2, it feels good to identify and connect with who you are. In this activity, you will use your character connection to prepare for specific emotional triggers. You will see that by remembering three powerful traits, you can quickly shift your emotional state from negative to positive. This activity may seem easy on paper; however, the process of recalling your traits under emotional discomfort requires repetitive practice. To do this, you must actively remind yourself each time you face a trigger. Also, be strategic in your trait selection by choosing the ones that will help you combat the specific situation. As a result, you will become more resilient in your performance and have a reliable way to maintain your self-esteem.

LET'S TAKE ACTION

- [ ] Read the first 3 triggers and identify which emotion(s) you feel.
- [ ] Record your own trigger in the 4th box and identify which emotion(s) you feel.
- [ ] Review your character traits from Activity 4.1 and select 3 that will prepare you to combat each specific trigger.
- [ ] Identify which emotion(s) you feel while connecting with your 3 traits.
- [ ] Determine what you can do to remember your 3 traits in the moment.

TRIGGER	EMOTION(S)
I GOT YELLED AT	🙂

> REMEMBER WHO YOU ARE <

I AM...	*I AM...*	*I AM...*

 Which emotion(s) do you feel when reading your three character traits?

Here are some strategies to help you remember your traits in the moment:

- *Write your traits on a flashcard and keep in your bag*
- *Wear a rubber band as a reminder of your traits*

REMEMBER MY CHARACTER TRAITS

TRIGGER
I MADE A MISTAKE

> ## EMOTION(S)

> ## REMEMBER WHO YOU ARE <

I AM...   I AM...   I AM...

 Which emotion(s) do you feel when reading your three character traits?

TRIGGER
I AM LOSING

> ## EMOTION(S)

> ## REMEMBER WHO YOU ARE <

I AM...   I AM...   I AM...

 Which emotion(s) do you feel when reading your three character traits?

TRIGGER

> ## EMOTION(S)

> ## REMEMBER WHO YOU ARE <

I AM...   I AM...   I AM...

 Which emotion(s) do you feel when reading your three character traits?

STRENGTHEN MY CHARACTER TRAITS

LET'S TALK

In addition to using character traits as an emotional management tool, they can also provide you with motivation to make behavioral changes. For example, you may want to develop patience, confidence, or courage. Now this doesn't mean that you never show these traits — it just means that you would like to demonstrate them more often. To accomplish this task, you will honestly assess your current negative behaviors and prepare yourself to make the desired changes. In time, you will realize that it's emotionally rewarding to both demonstrate and build character — and you will move closer to being the person and performer you are striving to be.

LET'S TAKE ACTION

- [ ] Review the character list from Activity 4.1 and select any 3 positive (+) traits that you would like to strengthen.
- [ ] Rate the % of time that you currently demonstrate each trait.
- [ ] Determine the opposite of each positive trait.
- [ ] Identify the triggers that cause you to demonstrate the negative (-) character trait.
- [ ] Determine what you can do to strengthen each (+) trait.

+ Character Trait I want to strengthen:

E F SHADE IN AMOUNT

% OF THE TIME

− What is the opposite of your + Character Trait?

I am triggered to be _____ ,

when _____

I can strengthen _____

by, _____

STRENGTHEN MY CHARACTER TRAITS

+ Character Trait I want to strengthen:

SHADE IN
AMOUNT

%
OF
THE
TIME

− What is the opposite of your + Character Trait?

I am triggered to be ,

when

I can strengthen

by,

+ Character Trait I want to strengthen:

E   F
SHADE IN
AMOUNT

%
OF
THE
TIME

− What is the opposite of your + Character Trait?

I am triggered to be ,

when

I can strengthen

by,

CHARACTER WEEKLY GOALS

When I *make a mistake* ,

I will remember that I am *smart* ,

competitive , and *determined* .

When I ,

I will remember that I am ,

, and .

When I ,

I will remember that I am ,

, and .

I want to be *disciplined* , so

I will *focus on my goal to push me through my discomfort* .

I want to be , so

I will .

I want to be , so

I will .

UNIT CHALLENGE

Are YOU up for the challenge?!

Ask a role model or someone you admire to discuss their character traits. Ask them how they established these traits and what they have learned about themselves in the process. What piece of advice would they have for you as you continue your journey to develop your own character?

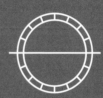

I WANT,
I WILL,
I CAN,
I AM.

MY GRATITUDE

"BY CULTIVATING GRATEFULNESS, WE ARE FREED FROM ENVY OVER WHAT WE DON'T HAVE OR WHO WE ARE NOT. IT DOESN'T MAKE LIFE PERFECT, BUT WITH GRATITUDE COMES THE REALIZATION THAT RIGHT NOW, IN THIS MOMENT, WE HAVE ENOUGH, ARE ENOUGH."
- ROBERT EMMONS

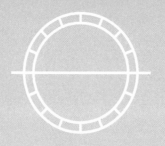

MY GRATITUDE

INTRODUCTION

Think about the performers you admire — the ones who stand out as excellent in their field. You might bring to mind their biggest accomplishments or best moments. What did they do or say when they achieved something great? Did they point to a teammate who helped them succeed? Did they thank their parents, coaches, or teammates in the post-game interview? Did they give a shout-out to a mentor or someone who supported them when they accepted an award? You may think that it is easy for a great performer to have gratitude, but the interesting fact is that gratitude can help you become a great performer.

As you've learned in the Emotional Management Framework, your performance is directly affected by your arousal, emotions, and thoughts. When stressed, you have learned to regulate this response with breathing techniques and by focusing on your WELL, core values, and character traits. In this section you will learn another powerful skill that trains your brain to remain in a calm state: the practice of gratitude. In fact, the expression or feeling of gratitude has the ability to reduce blood pressure, promote sleep, inspire healthy behaviors, and protect against illness and fatigue. These positive physical effects make it the perfect tool to keep you primed and ready to respond to the natural stressors in your performance environment.

Developing a practice of gratitude can also ignite positive emotions, strengthen character traits, and develop relationships that lead to personal satisfaction and performance success. For example, when you look for the good and express gratitude in a difficult situation, you will feel more optimistic, strengthen your resilience, and ultimately perform to your best ability. Or consider what would happen if you showed gratitude toward your teammates. I imagine that your relationships would improve and the team would become more cohesive. As you can see, it is undeniable that gratitude has a strong ability to improve performance. But first, you must use this section of your workbook and train yourself to develop a practice.

MY GRATITUDE ACTIVITY LOG

Check the box when you complete the activity.

- ☐ **READ //** My Gratitude Introduction
- ☐ **ACTIVITY 5.1 //** Identify My Gratitude
- ☐ **ACTIVITY 5.2 //** Access My Gratitude
- ☐ **ACTIVITY 5.3 //** Igniting My Gratitude
- ☐ **ACTIVITY 5.4 //** Strengthen My Gratitude
- ☐ **ACTIVITY 5.5 //** My Gratitude Goals

DAILY ACTION TRACKER

Make a mark on each day that you complete the activity.

Visited **MY WELL**

Practiced **BREATHING**

IDENTIFY MY GRATITUDE

LET'S TALK The first place to start when building a practice of gratitude is to acknowledge the people and relationships in your life that have affected you in a positive way. This may be difficult at first, but with practice, you'll get better at recognizing the big and small ways others contribute to your well-being or success. Think about your teammates, coaches, family, mentors, and friends. Who is there with an encouraging word or gesture? Who provides the practical support you need, like rides or equipment? Who has helped you grow as an individual or makes every situation more fun simply by being present?

LET'S TAKE ACTION

- [ ] Describe why you are grateful for each person.
- [ ] Write about a memorable moment when you felt grateful for that person.

IDENTIFY MY GRATITUDE

I AM GRATEFUL

I am grateful for my coach...

I am grateful for my teammates...

I am grateful for my parents/
support system...

I am grateful for...

(fill in the blank)

ACCESS MY GRATITUDE

LET'S TALK

To further access the powerful effects of gratitude, this activity will ask you to look for the good in various situations. This is easier to do when the situation is positive, but glimmers of good can also be found in difficult times. For example, maybe you got injured and had to watch your team perform from the sidelines. When looking for the positive, you may see that this experience gave you the opportunity to learn through observation, overcome difficult emotions, and show support to your teammates. During this activity, be thoughtful and optimistic in your responses for stronger performance effects.

LET'S TAKE ACTION!

- ☐ Read each question and answer with detail.
- ☐ Read each statement about a difficult situation and identify what you are grateful for.
- ☐ Identify which emotion(s) you feel while connecting with your gratitude.

What is your happiest childhood memory performing?	What is your favorite memory of someone cheering you on?
☺	☺
What future opportunity are you grateful for?	**What resources do you have access to in your performance environment?**
☺	☺

ACCESS MY GRATITUDE

When something happened to me that I didn't want, I was grateful...	When my performance didn't progress at the rate I wanted, I was grateful...
During a difficult situation I was grateful...	When I didn't achieve my goal, I was grateful...

IGNITE MY GRATITUDE

LET'S TALK

In order to truly ignite, or catch fire to your practice of gratitude, you will need to believe in its powerful effects. In this activity you will identify HOW your practice of gratitude will influence change. In other words, what will happen as a result of your gratitude practice? For example, I am grateful for the support during my ACL recovery, which has helped me to be more resilient to injuries. Or maybe I feel grateful for being named captain, because I can influence others by being a humble and supportive leader. As you reflect and record each effect, connect with how it feels. You will find that gratitude produces positive changes and it's therefore a beneficial practice for your performance success and enjoyment.

LET'S TAKE ACTION!

☐ Read each statement and consider the effects of practicing gratitude.

☐ Identify which emotion(s) you feel while connecting with the results

WHEN I PRACTICE GRATITUDE

I WILL BE MORE RESILIENT TO...

😊 Which emotion(s) will you feel as you ignite gratitude?

WHEN I PRACTICE GRATITUDE

I WILL INFLUENCE OTHERS BY...

😊 Which emotion(s) will you feel as you ignite gratitude?

IGNITE MY GRATITUDE

WHEN I PRACTICE GRATITUDE

I WILL BE LESS UPSET BY...

Which emotion(s) will you feel as you ignite gratitude?

WHEN I PRACTICE GRATITUDE

I WILL ACHIEVE...

Which emotion(s) will you feel as you ignite gratitude?

WHEN I PRACTICE GRATITUDE

I WILL FEEL BETTER ABOUT...

Which emotion(s) will you feel as you ignite gratitude?

WHEN I PRACTICE GRATITUDE

I WILL GET ALONG BETTER WITH...

Which emotion(s) will you feel as you ignite gratitude?

STRENGTHEN MY GRATITUDE

LET'S TALK

If you think about it, the opposite of expressing gratitude is to focus on the negative and complain. And it can be challenging to get out of this mindset. In this activity, you will reflect and identify the things that you complain about the most. You will then transform your perspective and take action to strengthen your practice of gratitude. As a result, you will feel more optimism, joy, and determination in your daily experiences.

LET'S TAKE ACTION!

- ☐ Determine 3 things that you complain about often and identify which emotion(s) you feel.
- ☐ Determine what you want to be grateful for.
- ☐ Develop an action plan to change your perspective of the situation.
- ☐ Identify which emotion(s) you feel when focusing on your action plan.

I COMPLAIN ABOUT:

☺ EMOTION(S):

I want to be grateful for

so I will take action by

☺ Which emotion(s) will you feel when focusing on your action plan?

STRENGTHEN MY GRATITUDE

I COMPLAIN ABOUT:

😃 EMOTION(S):

I want to be grateful for

so I will take action by

😃 Which emotion(s) will you feel when focusing on your action plan?

I COMPLAIN ABOUT:

😃 EMOTION(S):

I want to be grateful for

so I will take action by

😃 Which emotion(s) will you feel when focusing on your action plan?

GRATITUDE WEEKLY GOALS

I want to be grateful for *my opportunities to compete* so,
I will *recognize when I complain and re-focus on the gift of competition.*

I want to be grateful for so,
I will

I want to *practice gratitude* so
I will *visit my gratitude WELL every night before bed.*

I want to so
I will

UNIT CHALLENGE

Are YOU up for the challenge?!

Reach out to a coach, a teammate, a family member or someone else and tell them how grateful you are for them. It could be a phone call, a written note, or some other meaningful gesture.

I WANT,
I WILL,
I CAN,
I AM.

Congratulations! By completing the Foundations Workbook, you have established a set of healthy routines to keep you positive, focused, and motivated toward your goals. You have also learned an Emotional Management Framework and identified your triggers and their emotional, physical, and behavioral effects. And finally, you took control of your progress and challenged yourself to change your thoughts and behaviors.

As you move forward, we encourage you to routinely use your WELL, practice your breathing techniques, and set weekly goals or action plans. And when you face a trigger, think about the various skills that you've developed in each of the 5 sections. To summarize, you can call upon your WELL, apply your breathing techniques, uphold your values, remember your character traits, and practice gratitude. Altogether, the lessons from this workbook are a foundation for you to OWN WHO YOU ARE and progress in your journey. We wish you the best of luck!

"IT'S YOUR ROAD, AND YOURS ALONE.
OTHERS MAY WALK IT WITH YOU, BUT
NO ONE CAN WALK IT FOR YOU."

- RUMI

MY TOOLBOX

MY TOOLBOX

Throughout the Foundations Workbook you will be challenged to change your behaviors. To help you with this process we have created a toolbox, which is a list of actions for you to consider. When you see visit your toolbox, and select the action(s) that you believe will help you most. Keep in mind that you are not limited to this list — we encourage you to be personal and creative in your strategies to inspire development.

LET'S TAKE ACTION

- [ ] Read through the entire list of actions below.
- [ ] Identify the actions that you are drawn to the most (this may take some time).

Accept discomfort

Accept my emotions

Accept the things that I cannot control

Be aware of my emotions and how they feel within my body

Be aware of my triggers and behaviors

Communicate how I feel

Communicate my beliefs, needs, or desires

Express gratitude

Focus on my calming cue word or image

Focus on my next performance actions

Focus on what I am grateful for

Focus on what I can control

Re-focus on performing with my mantra

Remember moments from My WELL

Remember my dream goal (why I am doing this?)

Remember my top 3 character traits

Practice deep breathing

Prepare myself

Take 3 deep breaths to calm down

Trust the process

Trust myself

Trust my preparation

MY
EMOTION CHART

MY EMOTION CHART

LET'S TALK

You will learn in the Foundations Workbook that your e-motions are really energy moving through your body. This energy could either help or hurt your performance — which is why the Emotion Chart is the most important tool in this training process. In order to effectively manage your emotions, you must first identify and label the specific emotion(s) that you are feeling. To help you with this process, we have developed an Emotion Chart that is categorized by color. When you see 😃 visit your chart, scan the various emojis, and select the ones that you connect with the most. Keep in mind that there is no right or wrong emotion to be feeling — you are simply strengthening your emotional awareness and understanding.

LET'S TAKE ACTION !

- ☐ Review the emotion chart.
- ☐ Identify the emotion(s) that you most often feel triggered by (this may take some time).

I am repeatedly triggered by:
(Name the emotion and draw your own emoji)

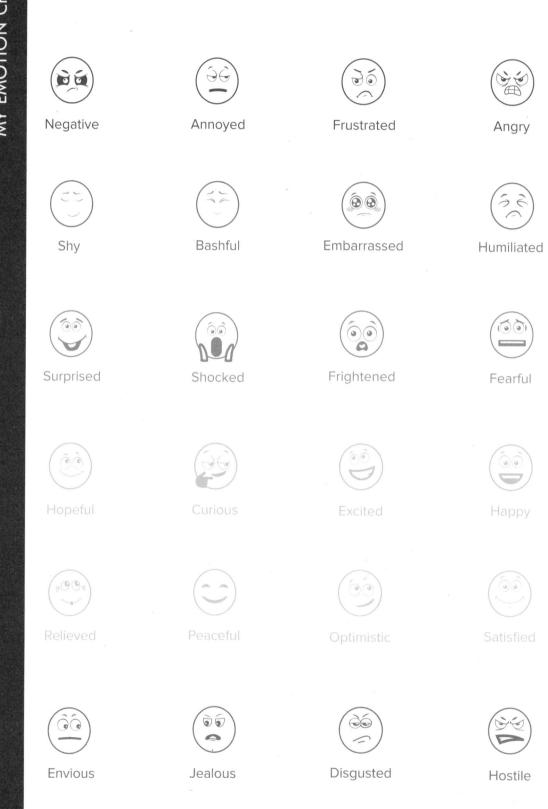

Negative	Annoyed	Frustrated	Angry
Shy	Bashful	Embarrassed	Humiliated
Surprised	Shocked	Frightened	Fearful
Hopeful	Curious	Excited	Happy
Relieved	Peaceful	Optimistic	Satisfied
Envious	Jealous	Disgusted	Hostile

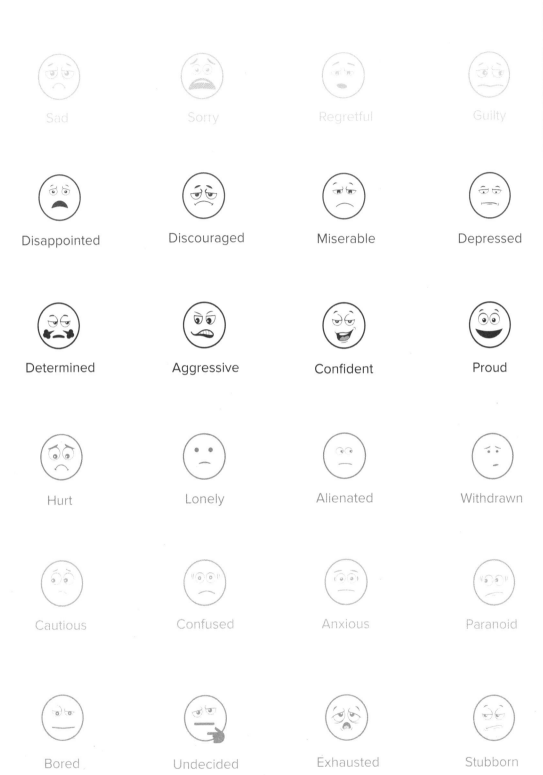

Sad

Sorry

Regretful

Guilty

Disappointed

Discouraged

Miserable

Depressed

Determined

Aggressive

Confident

Proud

Hurt

Lonely

Alienated

Withdrawn

Cautious

Confused

Anxious

Paranoid

Bored

Undecided

Exhausted

Stubborn

ABOUT THE AUTHORS

Amanda Ferranti, CMPC
Amanda Ferranti is the owner of Ferranti Empowerment with years of experience as a Certified Mental Performance Consultant for athletes, teams, and coaches. She is also a Princeton alumna, former professional soccer player, and licensed soccer coach, which has inspired her to make brain training more accessible for athletes and integrative for coaches. From personal and professional experiences, Amanda understands the importance of emotional management and is a passionate advocate of using sports to improve mental health in the world today.

Sean McMannis, Coach
Sean McMannis is a head soccer coach with over 17 years of coaching experience. From high schools, clubs, colleges to semi-pro, he has coached in California, Kansas, and Oklahoma. Sean holds multiple soccer licenses and earned a Master's Degree in Coaching and Athletic Administration from Concordia University. His dedication to each player reaches beyond just the technical and tactical aspects of the game. His passion is to strengthen and shape character through sports, using brain training techniques to develop the whole player and to unite the team. Sean has been married to his partner, Raeanna McMannis, since 2007. They have 2 daughters and 1 son.